"IF THERE IS A BOOK
THAT YOU WANT TO READ,
BUT IT HASN'T BEEN
WRITTEN YET,
YOU MUST BE THE ONE
TO WRITE IT."

Toni Morrison

DEDICATION

To my very first dog, Pepper,
who unknowingly
changed my entire life.

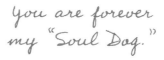

you are forever
my "Soul Dog."

ISBN: 978-0-578-56553-8

WHAT ABOUT the DOG ?

Everything You Need to Know
About My Dog's Care
(In Case I'm Not Around to Ask!)

Christine Ciana Calabrese

TESTIMONIALS

"This journal is packed with great information for any type of dog owner emergency...What About the Dog? is such an excellent book for anyone who has a dog and wants to make sure they are well taken care of..."

DR. CORINNE FISHER, VETERINARIAN,
LePar Animal Hospital, Hobart Animal Clinic and Crossroads Animal Hospital

"Christine has put a lot of thought into writing this book for dog owners. I think it is a must-have for anyone who loves their dogs!"

JUDI SCHNUR, OWNER,
Pawsitively Heaven Pet Resort

"This book combines all of the details your dogs' new guardians [would] need to know along with incredible tidbits of advice to help make the transition as easy as possible for your dog AND their new caregiver. You owe it to your dogs to buy this book!"

RANDA LYN CLARK, OWNER,
Tailchasers Incorporated and Barrington Pet Resort

DISCLAIMER

This book is not intended as a substitute for the medical advice of veterinarians or the behavioral advice of professional dog trainers and/or animal behaviorists. The reader should always consult a professional in matters relating to their dog's physical and/or mental health and particularly with respect to any symptoms that may require diagnosis or medical attention.

Table of Contents

ACKNOWLEDGMENTS

Special thanks to the following groups and individuals who encouraged the publication and promotion of this book:

- Natasha Skertich, for providing invaluable editing contributions and constructive feedback.

- Susan Donner and all of the tireless rescuers of the Lost and Found Cats and Dogs on the South/Southwest Side of Chicago Facebook Group

- Debby Collings of Petlink and Datamars microchip scanners

- Susan Taney of Lost Dogs Illinois

- Stacey Edge of MOMENTUM Creative Integration for providing invaluable guidance and breathing life into this book.

- Sharon Sprague of OK Silly Ink for her cover design contributions

- My attorney, Guy Youman, for his guidance on this project

- I would like to express my appreciation to the following members of Chicago's Spoken Word Community for their gifts of encouragement and positivity: Markell Thompson, Christian Bowie, Deidre Devance, Shameeka Shavers, Ollie Woods, Jamie Honeybee, and Karisa Tyler. These artists are the most uplifting individuals I know. "PERIODT!"

"This is a book rooted in the belief that our dogs are members of our family. In the event of unexpected circumstances, this book is to be used as an instrument to help your dog transition to a new home with as little stress as possible; the personal details you provide about your dog in this book will help guide your beloved dog's new caregiver, acting as a thoughtful instruction manual. Hopefully, you will never need this book for its intended purpose, in which case you may enjoy this book as a keepsake: a detailed diary of all of the funny, quirky, loving, and sometimes even annoying habits of your beloved family member...your dog."

JEAN LAZARRO, PRESIDENT,
Cry For Help Rescue

"I am not a veterinarian, dog trainer, animal behaviorist, or pet psychic. I don't whisper to dogs. I am, however, a pet parent myself, and I love my dogs as if they were my own children; the creation of this journal was my way of doing my best to ensure that they would be cared for in the most thoughtful way possible, by someone else, were I to become unable to care for them myself any longer. The Helpful Tips in between sections are tidbits of information I've learned over the past decade of working with dogs, which have served me well both personally and professionally. They are only suggestions and by no means should ever replace the recommendations of your veterinarian or behaviorist. I also highly encourage consulting an estate planning attorney to discuss the best way to financially preplan for your dog's extended care."

Warmly,
Christine Ciana Calabrese

7 WAYS TO GET THE MOST OUT OF THIS BOOK

1. This book is designed to accommodate information for two dogs that are being rehomed to the same household. If you have more than two dogs, or know that the dogs will be rehomed separately, please consider acquiring additional copies of this book, this way all caregivers are ensured to have the proper information.

2. Fill this book out as soon as possible.

3. Choose your dog's caregiver wisely and have a discussion with that person as to your specific wishes.

4. Tell your dog's caregiver about this book and where you will keep it. Consider keeping this book in plain view so that it can be easily referenced in case of an emergency. You may also want to discuss additional important paperwork (e.g., wills, trusts, insurance, etc.) as it pertains to your dog's care and financial support.

5. Have a successor caregiver listed for your dog in the event that circumstances change.

6. Review and update the information in this book as changes occur; this is especially important as your dog ages and/or develops potential medical or behavioral conditions.

7. IMPORTANT: MAKE SURE YOUR DOG'S MICROCHIP AND DOG TAG INFORMATION IS UP TO DATE.

6 WAYS TO INTRODUCE A DOG TO A NEW HOME

Introducing any dog to a new home is stressful, but there are a few steps you can take to make for a more comfortable transition.

1. Don't introduce the dog to the entire house all at once: choose a room or two for the first few days to let the dog get acclimated to all of the new smells and sounds of the new home. Baby gates are very helpful for creating safe boundaries within the home.

2. Study the dog's history, if known, and determine whether the dog has an aversion to children or other animals. If so, modifications will need to be made since it is unreasonable to assume that the dog will acclimate to these aversions. Even if the dog does not have a known aversion to children or other animals, it is advisable to initially limit all interactions between the dog and children or other animals. These introductions should occur gradually and on a limited basis to ensure the children's and the dog's safety and comfort.

3. Create a "safe space" that is not accessible to children or other animals that the dog can retreat to if he or she feels frightened or needs space. This space can be a travel carrier or crate, LEFT OPEN, but covered on three sides with a blanket and comfortable bedding inside, placed in a quiet part of the house that the dog can readily access. Stressed and fearful dogs are prone to urinate and defecate more frequently, so take this into consideration when choosing a room to let the dog settle into; a non-carpeted laundry room or spare bathroom may be a preferable selection. Stressed dogs also may be more prone to destructive behavior, so be sure to have plenty of toys and bones available in their room for them to chew on. Caution must be used when selecting the size of toys and bones: always choose oversized, chewable items to avoid choking hazards.

4. When dealing with dogs, EXERCISE will be your most important tool in alleviating their stress. If the dog is physically capable and healthy, a walk several times a day for the first few days will help the dog expend nervous energy.

5. With any new pet, establish a routine as soon as possible. Animals appreciate patterns and consistency just as humans do. Consistency in feeding times, water bowl placement, crate location, and walk times will help your new dog become comfortable more quickly.

6. Be patient and be calm. In time, the dog will adapt, but animals are very perceptive and are affected by others' energy and emotional states, so it is very important to be as calm as possible during this transition. If the dog seems to be having difficulty settling in, consult your veterinarian and/or a reputable animal behaviorist.

MY DOG(S)

and

Add photos here!

In case of emergency, please answer the following questions for the immediate care of your dog(s).

OWNER

Name:

Address:

Phone:

E-mail:

CO-OWNER (If applicable)

Name:

Address:

Phone:

E-mail:

Notes:

Designated Caregiver(s) for My Dog(s)

This is the person who is authorized to take my dog(s) and this book in case of emergency.

Name of dog(s) being rehomed:

Caregiver's name:

Address:

Phone:

E-mail:

Successor Caregiver(s) for My Dog(s)

This is the person who is authorized to take my dog(s) and this book should the caregiver(s) listed above be unwilling or unable to care for my dog(s).

Name of dog(s) being rehomed:

Caregiver's name:

Address:

Phone:

E-mail:

Notes:

11

Name of dog being rehomed:

My dog is on medication: ❑ YES   ❑ NO

If YES, name and location of medication:

My dog's food is located:

My dog normally wears a collar inside the house.   ❑ YES   ❑ NO

If NO, the collar can be found in this location in my home:

If my situation or hospitalization is only temporary, I would prefer that my dog stays in my home: ❑ YES   ❑ NO

If my dog must leave my home, please be sure to take the following items with him/her (e.g., bed, toys, food, bowls, etc.):

The items accompanying my dog can be found in these locations in my home:

Name of dog being rehomed:

My dog is on medication: ❑ YES   ❑ NO

If YES, name and location of medication:

My dog's food is located:

My dog normally wears a collar
inside the house.   ❑ YES   ❑ NO

If NO, the collar can be found in this location in my home:

If my situation or hospitalization is
only temporary, I would prefer that   ❑ YES   ❑ NO
my dog stays in my home:

If my dog must leave my home, please be sure to take the
following items with him/her (e.g., bed, toys, food, bowls, etc.):

The items accompanying my dog can be found in these
locations in my home:

Animal hospital name:

Veterinarian name:

Address:

Phone:

Hours:

Name of dog being rehomed:

Breed:

Sex:

Color: Weight:

Overview of medical conditions and/or diagnoses:

List medications and dosages:

Date of last rabies vaccination:

Date of other vaccinations: *(If applicable)*

Bordetella: Canine Influenza:

Distemper: Giardia:

Hepatitis: Leptospirosis:

Lyme: Other:

Date of last heartworm test:

I treat my dog for fleas and ticks: *(Circle one)*
- Monthly   Seasonally
- As Needed   Not at All

Flea and tick prevention brand:

Date of last dental cleaning:

My dog is spayed/neutered: ❑ YES   ❑ NO

My dog is microchipped: ❑ YES   ❑ NO

Microchip company:

Microchip ID number:

Phone:

Registered person:

Address:

Phone:

My dog has bred: ❑ YES   ❑ NO

Notes:

Animal hospital name:

Veterinarian name:

Address:

Phone:

Hours:

Name of dog being rehomed:

Breed:

Sex:

Color: Weight:

Overview of medical conditions and/or diagnoses:

List medications and dosages:

Date of last rabies vaccination:

Date of other vaccinations: *(If applicable)*

Bordetella: Canine Influenza:

Distemper: Giardia:

Hepatitis: Leptospirosis:

Lyme: Other:

Date of last heartworm test:

I treat my dog for fleas and ticks: *(Circle one)*

    Monthly   Seasonally

    As Needed   Not at All

Flea and tick prevention brand:

Date of last dental cleaning:

My dog is spayed/neutered: ❏ YES   ❏ NO

My dog is microchipped: ❏ YES   ❏ NO

Microchip company:

Microchip ID number:

Phone:

Registered person:

Address:

Phone:

My dog has bred: ❏ YES   ❏ NO

Notes:

Helpful Tips!

- The preceding information can be obtained in more detail from the dog's veterinarian. If the caregiver will be using a different veterinarian due to proximity from the caregiver's home, the caregiver will need to request that the dog's current veterinarian copy and send the dog's medical records to the new veterinarian.

- If you are one of those pet parents who are concerned about potentially over-vaccinating your dog, speak to your veterinarian about having a titers test; a titer is a measurement of a specific antibody in the blood. This blood test will indicate if your dog still has adequate immunity to a certain disease from a previous vaccination.

- Do not forget to tell your dog's caregiver to update the microchip information when they take on caring for your dog. Call the microchip company listed in this book and update changes of address and phone numbers. Also, be sure to change the contact information on your dog's collar tags. If microchip information is not provided in this book, a veterinarian or animal shelter should be able to scan the dog and tell you which company has registered the microchip.

- Always have two different phone numbers on your dog's ID tag, in the event one number is changed or the individual is unreachable.

- If you live alone with your dog, consider having a keychain and/or a wallet notecard made stating that your dog is home alone, in case of emergency; also have a phone number available for a first responder to contact.

- Additionally, you can purchase static cling window decals for your home so that in case of a fire, first responders are aware that your dog is inside.

Notes:

LEGAL DOCUMEMTS

Have you prepared an estate plan? ❏ YES ❏ NO

Where are your estate planning documents located?

What documents are you including in your estate plan?

What is the name and contact information of your attorney?

Have you purchased life insurance? ❏ YES ❏ NO

If YES, name of insurance company?

Where is a copy of your life insurance policy?

NOTE: Your veterinarian will have copies of your dog's medical records, but if you have additional documentation that you would like your caregiver to have, please include the type and location of those documents. If you have pet insuranc your veterinarian will also have those records, but itis important to provide policy numbers, copies of policies, and contact information to your caregiver.

Notes:

Name of dog being rehomed:

My dog likes to be picked up: ❑ YES ❑ NO

My dog does NOT like these areas touched: (Circle all)
Ears Mouth
Paws Other:

My dog is fearful overall: ❑ YES ❑ NO

My dog has bitten out of fear in the past: ❑ YES ❑ NO

My dog has the following specific phobias:

This helps to alleviate my dog's fears:

My dog has medication for specific phobias: ❑ YES ❑ NO

If YES, please name medication and dosage:

My dog wears a Thundershirt™: ❑ YES ❑ NO

If YES, what size?

My dog wears an Anxiety Wrap™: ❑ YES ❑ NO

If YES, what size?

Name of dog being rehomed:		
My dog likes to be picked up:	❑ YES	❑ NO
My dog does NOT like these areas touched: *(Circle all)* Ears Mouth Paws Other:		
My dog is fearful overall:	❑ YES	❑ NO
My dog has bitten out of fear in the past:	❑ YES	❑ NO
My dog has the following specific phobias:		
This helps to alleviate my dog's fears:		
My dog has medication for specific phobias:	❑ YES	❑ NO
If YES, please name medication and dosage:		
My dog wears a Thundershirt™:	❑ YES	❑ NO
If YES, what size?		
My dog wears an Anxiety Wrap™:	❑ YES	❑ NO
If YES, what size?		

🐾 Speak to your veterinarian about incorporating holistic aids such as lavender oil or any natural supplements to help calm your dog, especially during the transition period and other stressful situations.

🐾 White noise such as fans and air conditioners can be used in the house to drown out distressing outside noises. You can also purchase white noise machines and download similar apps designed for infants that may have a similar positive effect on dogs. If music is used, studies published in the *Journal of Veterinary Behavior* have shown classical music to be most soothing. Remember, not all music or background noise is created equally. Relaxing music to humans may not be relaxing to dogs. Raucous TV or radio can have the opposite effect of what you are trying to accomplish.

🐾 A Thundershirt™ or similar compression clothing for dogs may help alleviate your dog's anxiety and can be purchased at almost any retail pet supply outlet.

🐾 Rigorous exercise will be your greatest tool in combating anxiety. Daily walks coupled with extra walks prior to stressful situations (provided your dog is healthy enough for such activity) will be extremely helpful in calming your dog. We will discuss dog walks further in the chapter titled *Exercise*.

Notes:

Name of dog being rehomed:

Nickname:

Primary language:

Secondary language:

My dog responds to hand signals: ❑ YES   ❑ NO

If YES, please list commands:

Please list any quirky behaviors and/or unique traits:

Name of dog being rehomed:

Nickname:

Primary language:

Secondary language:

My dog responds to hand signals: ❏ YES ❏ NO

If YES, please list commands:

Please list any quirky behaviors and/or unique traits:

Name of dog being rehomed:

My dog eats this brand of food:

You can purchase it at:

The quantity of food at each meal is:

I add this additive to the food:

You can purchase the additive at:

Do you leave the food out all day?	❑ YES	❑ NO

If NO, what are the feeding times?

My dog has food aggression:	❑ YES	❑ NO

If YES, specific to: *(Circle all)*

    Dogs   Children

    Humans   Other:

I make my dog sit before eating:	❑ YES	❑ NO
My dog uses a slow feeder dog bowl:	❑ YES	❑ NO

My dog's favorite treats are:

List any special feeding instructions:

Helpful Tips!

🐾 The Humane Society has come out with a list of foods that are toxic to your dog, which include, but are not limited to: onions, avocados, coffee, grapes, raisins, and chocolate. Additionally, many additives used in human food are harmful to dogs including **xylitol**, which is an artificial sweetener commonly found in sugar-free gum. Xylitol can be found in **certain brands of peanut butter**, so double check your ingredient labels if you give your dog peanut butter as a treat. Xylitol can also be found in human toothpaste, which is one of the many reasons that you should only brush your dog's teeth with toothpaste specifically made for dogs. For a complete list of foods, please consult your veterinarian. You can also reference the Humane Society's website through the following link:

⇨ m.humanesociety.org/animals/resources/tips/foods_poisonous_to_pets.html

🐾 Remember, because the bulk of dogs' diets consist of dry kibble and dry cookies as treats, dogs can absolutely benefit from the vitamins and fiber found in fresh fruit and vegetables. For a list of beneficial foods for your dogs, please consult your veterinarian. We have also provided additional link:

⇨ m.petmd.com/dog/slideshows/nutrition/10-best-fruits-and-vegetables-dogs

🐾 It is important that barrel-chested dogs do not eat too quickly, particularly if fed only once a day, because they can be susceptible to a potentially deadly gastrointestinal condition known as Bloat. Owners can educate themselves on the symptoms of Bloat by consulting with their veterinarians. We have provided a resourceful article published by the *Whole Dog Journal* on the topic:

➡ whole-dog-journal.com/issues/8_1/features/Dog-Bloat-Causes-Signs-and-Symptoms_15682-1.html

🐾 Not all dog foods are created equally. Educate yourself on the dog food industry; there are several excellent resources available including *Food Pets Die For* by Ann Martin. It is a shocking exposé on the industry with helpful tips on how to read ingredient labels on your dog's food, and even how to home cook your dog's food yourself. As always, consult with your veterinarian to review your dog's specific health needs.

Notes:

Name of dog being rehomed:		
My dog is high energy:	❏ YES	❏ NO

If YES, my dog needs extra exercise through: *(Circle all)*

> Treadmill   Jogging with a human
> Weighted backpack   Playing fetch
> Running alongside a bicycle with attachment
> Other:

I take my dog for walks:	❏ YES	❏ NO

If NO, is there a medical reason for this?

If YES, how often and how far?

If YES, my dog is walked on a: *(Circle all)*

> Regular collar   Prong collar
> Harness   Gentle leader
> Choke collar   Lead with muzzle
> Other:

My dog walks on this side of me:	❏ RIGHT	❏ LEFT
My dog walks off leash:	❏ YES	❏ NO
My dog goes out in the rain:	❏ YES	❏ NO

In the backyard, my dog needs a fence that is a minimum of _____ feet high.

My dog has climbed or jumped fences in the past:	❏ YES	❏ NO
My dog has dug under fences:	❏ YES	❏ NO
My dog likes to swim in lakes:	❏ YES	❏ NO

Name of dog being rehomed:

| My dog is high energy: | ❑ YES | ❑ NO |

If YES, my dog needs extra exercise through: *(Circle all)*

Treadmill   Jogging with a human
Weighted backpack   Playing fetch
Running alongside a bicycle with attachment
Other:

| I take my dog for walks: | ❑ YES | ❑ NO |

If NO, is there a medical reason for this?

If YES, how often and how far?

If YES, my dog is walked on a: *(Circle all)*

Regular collar   Prong collar
Harness   Gentle leader
Choke collar   Lead with muzzle
Other:

| My dog walks on this side of me: | ❑ RIGHT | ❑ LEFT |

| My dog walks off leash: | ❑ YES | ❑ NO |

| My dog goes out in the rain: | ❑ YES | ❑ NO |

In the backyard, my dog needs a fence that is a minimum of _____ feet high.

| My dog has climbed or jumped fences in the past: | ❑ YES | ❑ NO |

| My dog has dug under fences: | ❑ YES | ❑ NO |

| My dog likes to swim in lakes: | ❑ YES | ❑ NO |

🐾 Exercising your dog has several benefits: first and foremost, exercise, in addition to a moderate diet, will help keep your dog at a healthy weight. Pet obesity is an increasing problem in the United States. Secondly, exercise will minimize your dog's anxiety and boredom. Remember, there is a correlation between destructive behaviors in dogs and dogs that do not get enough adequate, daily exercise.

🐾 Just as with human exercise regimens, there are 5 major variables that you can manipulate to increase your dog's workout: Frequency, Intensity, Time, Type, and Speed, or F.I.T.T.S.

Frequency: how many times a day do you exercise your dog?

Intensity: is your dog wearing a weighted dog backpack or pulling a sled?

Time: how long of a period do you exercise your dog?

Type: what kind of exercises do you do with your dog? For example, are you hiking hills, swimming, jogging, or running an obstacle course?

Speed: how long does it take you to complete a specified exercise session?

🐾 Start making changes gradually to your dog's exercise routine, and always consult your veterinarian before starting a new exercise program, especially if your dog has a condition, is elderly, has a current injury, or has had a past surgery.

At the time of this book development, several cases of dog deaths were reported after swimming in lakes, according to various news outlets; the causes of death were attributed to blue-green algae toxicity. The toxin released from blue-green algae is found in warm, stagnant water and most prevalent in the summer season. It causes liver failure and death can occur in as little as 15-minutes after ingestion.

If you enjoy walking your dog(s) in woodland areas, please remain vigilant about the presence of ticks; talk to your veterinarian about natural tick repellents such as cedar oil, as well as a potential vaccination against Lyme Disease. Don't forget to thoroughly inspect your dog(s) for ticks following a walk through woodland areas or fields with tall grass.

Notes:

Name of dog being rehomed:

My dog is only left alone for a maximum of _____ hours.

My dog is crated when I leave:	❑ YES	❑ NO

My dog has access to the entire house while I'm away:	❑ YES	❑ NO

If NO, what areas are off limits?

I leave a TV or radio on for my dog:	❑ YES	❑ NO

I leave certain lights on for my dog:	❑ YES	❑ NO

If YES, please explain:

I give my dog special items before I leave:	❑ YES	❑ NO

If YES, please explain:

My dog has a dog walker that comes during the day:	❑ YES	❑ NO

If YES, answer the following questions about your dog walker:

How often does the dog walker come?

How long does the dog walker take care of your dog?

What is the agreed upon payment?

Dog walker's contact information:

Name of dog being rehomed:

My dog is only left alone for a maximum of _____ hours.

My dog is crated when I leave:	❏ YES	❏ NO

My dog has access to the entire house while I'm away: ❏ YES ❏ NO

If NO, what areas are off limits?

I leave a TV or radio on for my dog:	❏ YES	❏ NO
I leave certain lights on for my dog:	❏ YES	❏ NO

If YES, please explain:

I give my dog special items before I leave: ❏ YES ❏ NO

If YES, please explain:

My dog has a dog walker that comes during the day: ❏ YES ❏ NO

If YES, answer the following questions about your dog walker:

How often does the dog walker come?

How long does the dog walker take care of your dog?

What is the agreed upon payment?

Dog walker's contact information:

Helpful Tips!

🐾 Separation anxiety can be a real problem for some dogs and their owners. Again, exercise will be your greatest tool in addressing this issue.

🐾 Dogs primarily become destructive out of boredom and frustration. A regimented exercise routine, followed by a meal, and topped off with an oversized bone or toy to chew on and comfortable bedding will help settle your dog down.

🐾 Again, if you leave on a radio or TV for your dog while away, be conscious of your selection. Quiet, calm and soothing sounds will serve your dog best.

🐾 If you must crate your dog while away, **DO NOT** leave your dog's collar on in the crate. The threat of a dog hanging himself or herself is real.

🐾 If you must be gone for long periods of time, consider getting yourself a professional pet sitter or dog walker to tend to your dog periodically. There are professional pet sitting organizations that pet sitters and dog walkers join to lend credibility to their businesses. These individuals are generally background checked, insured, and bonded.

🐾 **DO YOUR DUE DILIGENCE** in researching and interviewing prospective dog walkers and pet sitters. Regardless of the company who employs them or their professional affiliation, **ask to see referrals and reviews.** Never make assumptions about individuals you will be entrusting to care for your dog(s).

Notes:

Name of dog being rehomed:

My dog is professionally groomed:　　　❏ YES　　　❏ NO

Professional Grooming Information

Provide the name of your grooming salon and contact information for your groomer:

How often is your dog professionally groomed?

What does your groomer typically charge?

Additional services I request of my groomer:

NAIL TRIM	❏ YES	❏ NO
EAR CLEANING	❏ YES	❏ NO
ANAL GLANDS	❏ YES	❏ NO
TEETH BRUSHING	❏ YES	❏ NO
OTHER:	❏ YES	❏ NO

At Home Grooming Information

I wash my dog in the: *(Circle one)*

Tub　　　　　　　　Shower

Utility sink　　　　　Self Dog Wash at a facility

How often do you bathe your dog?

How often do you brush your dog's hair?

How often do you brush your dog's teeth?

Name of dog being rehomed:

My dog is professionally groomed: ❑ YES ❑ NO

Professional Grooming Information

Provide the name of your grooming salon and contact information for your groomer:

How often is your dog professionally groomed?

What does your groomer typically charge?

Additional services I request of my groomer:

NAIL TRIM	❑ YES	❑ NO
EAR CLEANING	❑ YES	❑ NO
ANAL GLANDS	❑ YES	❑ NO
TEETH BRUSHING	❑ YES	❑ NO
OTHER:	❑ YES	❑ NO

At Home Grooming Information

I wash my dog in the: (Circle one)

    Tub   Shower

    Utility sink   Self Dog Wash at a facility

How often do you bathe your dog?

How often do you brush your dog's hair?

How often do you brush your dog's teeth?

Helpful Tips!

🐾 Many dogs dislike going to the groomer. You can help curb their anxiety by exercising them prior to your appointment.

🐾 If you must select a new groomer, pay attention to details: Is the facility clean? How does the staff act toward the animals? Are you allowed to stay and watch what they do? It is okay to be extremely picky about who tends to your dog. Consider getting recommendations from friends and family as well as online reviews.

🐾 Most dogs do not like cage dryers; ask the groomer how they handle drying the dogs: Do they use hand blow dryers? Is it a timed (heated or cool air) dryer kennel?

🐾 If you clip your own dog's nails at home and you accidentally cut the dog's quick (the blood vessel inside the nail) and the dog starts to bleed, flour applied to the nail tip should stop the bleeding within a minute or two; if the bleeding continues, get to your veterinarian.

🐾 It is recommended that you brush your dog's teeth, as harmful tartar buildup will occur and could cause similar health problems that humans experience. You can purchase dog toothbrushes in varying shapes, sizes, and colors. An alternative to using a toothbrush is a finger brush, which is a rubber cover with imitation bristles that you wear on your index finger; it is a little less intimidating than a traditional toothbrush; however, if your dog is still reacting adversely, you can use plain gauze wrapped around your finger. Moisten the gauze with water and apply dog toothpaste.

🐾 Please keep in mind that when brushing a dog's teeth, you should only use toothpaste specifically made for dogs. As mentioned in the chapter *Diet and Feeding*, xylitol is an artificial sweetener found in human toothpaste and is harmful to dogs.

🐾 Remember, long-eared dogs are more susceptible to ear infections. Ask your veterinarian to show you the best way to clean your dog's ears and how frequently this should be done.

Notes:

Name of dog being rehomed:		
My dog is potty trained:	❏ YES	❏ NO
If YES, is there still an occasional accident?	❏ YES	❏ NO
My dog is trained to use bell chimes, or something similar, to signal he or she must go out:	❏ YES	❏ NO
My dog is potty-pad trained:	❏ YES	❏ NO
My dog responds to the following word or phrase when it is time to go potty:		
The longest my dog goes without a potty break is _____ hours.		
My dog wears diapers:	❏ YES	❏ NO
If YES, how often do you change the diapers?		
My dog wears a belly band:	❏ YES	❏ NO
My dog eats his/her own poop:	❏ YES	❏ NO
My dog ONLY poops during a walk:	❏ YES	❏ NO

Name of dog being rehomed:		
My dog is potty trained:	❑ YES	❑ NO
If YES, is there still an occasional accident?	❑ YES	❑ NO
My dog is trained to use bell chimes, or something similar, to signal he or she must go out:	❑ YES	❑ NO
My dog is potty-pad trained:	❑ YES	❑ NO
My dog responds to the following word or phrase when it is time to go potty:		
The longest my dog goes without a potty break is _____ hours.		
My dog wears diapers:	❑ YES	❑ NO
If YES, how often do you change the diapers?		
My dog wears a belly band:	❑ YES	❑ NO
My dog eats his/her own poop:	❑ YES	❑ NO
My dog ONLY poops during a walk:	❑ YES	❑ NO

Helpful Tips!

🐾 Periodically, take notice of your dog's urinating habits: Are they taking longer to urinate? Or urinating more frequently? Does the urine have a strong or fishy smell? Is your dog suddenly having accidents in the house? Are you noticing pink urine or drops of blood? If you see or suspect any of the above, consult your veterinarian immediately about bringing in a urine sample to check for a urinary tract infection.

🐾 If your dog develops incontinence and you opt to use "doggy diapers" or a disposable liner inside of cloth diapers, change the absorbent parts frequently or your dog can potentially develop urine burn, which is a painful skin condition from prolonged contact of urine on the skin.

Notes:

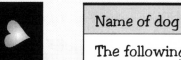

Name of dog being rehomed:

The following are specific triggers that cause my dog's disciplinary problems:

My disciplinary tool of choice for my dog is: *(Circle one)*

Spray bottle of water   Noise maker

Stern voice   Time Out

The disciplinary tool that should NOT be used on my dog is:

My dog has been muzzled: ❑ YES   ❑ NO

If YES, my dog has their own muzzle: ❑ YES   ❑ NO

Type of muzzle: ❑ NYLON   ❑ BASKET

Reason to wear muzzle:

Name of dog being rehomed:

The following are specific triggers that cause my dog's disciplinary problems:

My disciplinary tool of choice for my dog is: (Circle one)

Spray bottle of water   Noise maker

Stern voice   Time Out

The disciplinary tool that should NOT be used on my dog is:

My dog has been muzzled:	❏ YES	❏ NO
If YES, my dog has their own muzzle:	❏ YES	❏ NO
Type of muzzle:	❏ NYLON	❏ BASKET

Reason to wear muzzle:

❖ **NEVER HIT A DOG.** Using violence against a dog that already has aggression issues will only exacerbate the situation. Use extreme caution when choosing your method of discipline for dogs who are already fearful; noise makers and air horns can potentially cause further emotional damage. Consult a reputable positive reinforcement dog trainer or behaviorist for problems with your dog that you are unable to resolve on your own; they can help you determine which disciplinary techniques are most appropriate for your situation.

Notes:

SLEEPING ARRANGEMENTS

Name of dog being rehomed:

My dog has a normal bedtime of:

We usually get up at:

During the day, my dog likes to sleep (e.g., where, when, how):

At nighttime, my dog likes to sleep (e.g., where, when, how):

If the dog sleeps in bed with humans, does the dog have a preferred spot?

My dog likes to be under covers or inside pillows: ❑ YES ❑ NO

My dog requires assistance or stairs/ramp to get in and out of a human's bed: ❑ YES ❑ NO

Additional information or idiosyncrasies of my pet's sleeping habits (snoring, etc.):

Name of dog being rehomed:

My dog has a normal bedtime of:

We usually get up at:

During the day, my dog likes to sleep (e.g., where, when, how):

At nighttime, my dog likes to sleep (e.g., where, when, how):

If the dog sleeps in bed with humans, does the dog have a preferred spot?

My dog likes to be under covers or inside pillows:	❑ YES	❑ NO
My dog requires assistance or stairs/ramp to get in and out of a human's bed:	❑ YES	❑ NO

Additional information or idiosyncrasies of my pet's sleeping habits (snoring, etc.):

🐾 Be sure to articulate if your dog likes to sleep in hidden away places like inside pillowcases or closets so the caregiver doesn't panic if the dog isn't readily seen or found.

🐾 Use wise judgment in allowing toy dog breeds and/or puppies to sleep in the bed, particularly with children; injury or death can accidentally occur by rolling over the dog. In a similar respect, some dogs may be irritated by children moving around in the bed in the middle of the night. Although your dog might be comfortable sleeping with you and your children at this stage, your dog may not be comfortable sleeping with your caregiver or their family members. It is advisable to review the potential sleeping arrangements with the caregiver to ensure that your dog, the caregiver, and the caregiver's children are not put at risk during the night.

Notes:

Name of dog being rehomed:

My dog likes car rides: ❏ YES ❏ NO

My dog generally travels in the: *(Circle one)*
Front seat   Back seat
Rear of SUV   Other:

To keep my dog safe, my dog usually travels in a: *(Circle one)*
Hard carrier   Soft carrier   K9 car fence
Harness & seatbelt   Nothing   Other:

My dog gets carsick: ❏ YES ❏ NO

My dog is allowed to stick his or her head out of the window: ❏ YES ❏ NO

My dog needs assistance getting in and out of the car: ❏ YES ❏ NO

The following equipment is used to get my dog in and out of the vehicle: *(Circle one)*
Stairs   Ramp   Body sling

The protocol for traveling with my dog is (e.g., travels in a hard carrier in the back seat):

Name of dog being rehomed:

My dog likes car rides: ❑ YES ❑ NO

My dog generally travels in the: *(Circle one)*
    Front seat   Back seat
    Rear of SUV   Other:

To keep my dog safe, my dog usually travels in a: *(Circle one)*
Hard carrier   Soft carrier   K9 car fence
Harness & seatbelt   Nothing   Other:

My dog gets carsick: ❑ YES ❑ NO

My dog is allowed to stick his or her head out of the window: ❑ YES ❑ NO

My dog needs assistance getting in and out of the car: ❑ YES ❑ NO

The following equipment is used to get my dog in and out of the vehicle: *(Circle one)*
    Stairs   Ramp   Body sling

The protocol for traveling with my dog is (e.g., travels in a hard carrier in the back seat):

Helpful Tips!

🐾 Never leave your dog in a locked car with no air-conditioning in temperatures at 70 degrees F or above. Temperatures can rise as quickly as 20 degrees in 10 minutes. Dogs do not sweat like humans do and can overheat quickly and quite possibly die of heat stroke. As of August 2015, Illinois amended the Humane Care of Animals Act, making it a Class A misdemeanor, which is punishable by a fine of up to $2,500 or up to one year in jail. Details of this law can be found here:

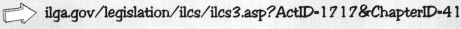 ilga.gov/legislation/ilcs/ilcs3.asp?ActID=1717&ChapterID=41

🐾 You may consider purchasing protective eyewear, such as Doggles™, for your dog for rides in the car or on motorcycles.

Notes:

Name of dog being rehomed:

My dog will wear dog clothing: ❏ YES ❏ NO

In extreme weather, I use the following to protect my dog:

BOOTIES: ❏ YES ❏ NO

PAW WAX: ❏ YES ❏ NO

EAR PROTECTION: ❏ YES ❏ NO

COAT: ❏ YES ❏ NO

SWEATER: ❏ YES ❏ NO

RAIN COAT: ❏ YES ❏ NO

I put a coat or sweater on my dog if the temperature falls below _____ degrees.

Name of dog being rehomed:

My dog will wear dog clothing: ❏ YES ❏ NO

In extreme weather, I use the following to protect my dog:

BOOTIES: ❏ YES ❏ NO

PAW WAX: ❏ YES ❏ NO

EAR PROTECTION: ❏ YES ❏ NO

COAT: ❏ YES ❏ NO

SWEATER: ❏ YES ❏ NO

RAIN COAT: ❏ YES ❏ NO

I put a coat or sweater on my dog if the temperature falls below _____ degrees.

Helpful Tips!

- Use extreme caution when choosing costumes and clothing for dogs involving elastic, particularly around the paws; loss of circulation is a real danger to extremities, which can potentially lead to loss of appendages.

- Short-haired breeds (e.g., bully breeds, Dobermans, etc.) can benefit from fleece-lined coverings in extreme cold due to natural leanness and lack of heavy fur.

- Some dogs have a strong aversion to clothing that has to go over the head and/or has sleeves. If you must put something on your dog, opt for a layover coat that attaches under the belly as an alternative. Velcro wears out over time, so it's a good idea to invest in additional Velcro strips that can be sewn onto your dog's clothing as needed.

Notes:

Name of dog being rehomed:			
My dog has been socialized with other dogs:	❑ YES	❑ NO	
My dog is good with bigger dogs:	❑ YES	❑ NO	❑ UNKNOWN
My dog is good with cats:	❑ YES	❑ NO	❑ UNKNOWN
My dog is good with small dogs:	❑ YES	❑ NO	❑ UNKNOWN
My dog is good with men:	❑ YES	❑ NO	❑ UNKNOWN
My dog is good with women:	❑ YES	❑ NO	❑ UNKNOWN
My dog is good with children:	❑ YES	❑ NO	❑ UNKNOWN
My dog is good with strangers coming to door:	❑ YES	❑ NO	❑ UNKNOWN
My dog will chase rabbits, squirrels, etc.:	❑ YES	❑ NO	❑ UNKNOWN
My dog will chase bicycles or motorcycles:	❑ YES	❑ NO	❑ UNKNOWN
My dog likes the mail delivery person:	❑ YES	❑ NO	❑ UNKNOWN

Please list any additional pets or individuals that your dog does NOT get along with:

List your dog's love interests and/or playmates:

List your dog's sworn enemies:

Name of dog being rehomed:			
My dog has been socialized with other dogs:	❏ YES	❏ NO	
My dog is good with bigger dogs:	❏ YES	❏ NO	❏ UNKNOWN
My dog is good with cats:	❏ YES	❏ NO	❏ UNKNOWN
My dog is good with small dogs:	❏ YES	❏ NO	❏ UNKNOWN
My dog is good with men:	❏ YES	❏ NO	❏ UNKNOWN
My dog is good with women:	❏ YES	❏ NO	❏ UNKNOWN
My dog is good with children:	❏ YES	❏ NO	❏ UNKNOWN
My dog is good with strangers coming to door:	❏ YES	❏ NO	❏ UNKNOWN
My dog will chase rabbits, squirrels, etc.:	❏ YES	❏ NO	❏ UNKNOWN
My dog will chase bicycles or motorcycles:	❏ YES	❏ NO	❏ UNKNOWN
My dog likes the mail delivery person:	❏ YES	❏ NO	❏ UNKNOWN

Please list any additional pets or individuals that your dog does NOT get along with:

List your dog's love interests and/or playmates:

List your dog's sworn enemies:

🐾 When introducing your dog to other dogs that will be visiting your home, keep in mind that it is best to conduct all introductions outside, off of your property, on neutral territory.

🐾 Socializing your dog, particularly at a young age, is essential in helping your dog learn proper etiquette among his or her peers. Dogs that do not get to socialize are more likely to grow up maladjusted.

Notes:

Name of dog being rehomed:		
My dog has special needs?	❑ YES	❑ NO

If YES, my dog: *(Circle all)*

Blind	Deaf	Diabetic
Epileptic	Paralyzed	Other:

My dog requires assistance up and down stairs:	❑ YES	❑ NO

If YES, my dog: *(Circle all)*

is carried	uses a body sling
uses a ramp	Other:

My dog wears a diaper:	❑ YES	❑ NO
My dog is prone to UTI´s:	❑ YES	❑ NO
My dog is prone to rashes or other skin conditions:	❑ YES	❑ NO
My dog uses a wheelchair:	❑ YES	❑ NO

If YES, how long is the dog in the wheelchair at any given time?

Company and contact information for where the wheelchair can be taken or sent for repairs:

Does the wheelchair have a warranty?	❑ YES	❑ NO
My dog has a different set of special needs than those listed above:	❑ YES	❑ NO

If YES, please explain:

Name of dog being rehomed: _____

| My dog has special needs? | ❏ YES | ❏ NO |

If YES, my dog: (Circle all)

| Blind | Deaf | Diabetic |
| Epileptic | Paralyzed | Other: |

| My dog requires assistance up and down stairs: | ❏ YES | ❏ NO |

If YES, my dog: (Circle all)

| is carried | uses a body sling |
| uses a ramp | Other: |

| My dog wears a diaper: | ❏ YES | ❏ NO |

| My dog is prone to UTI's: | ❏ YES | ❏ NO |

| My dog is prone to rashes or other skin conditions: | ❏ YES | ❏ NO |

| My dog uses a wheelchair: | ❏ YES | ❏ NO |

If YES, how long is the dog in the wheelchair at any given time?

Company and contact information for where the wheelchair can be taken or sent for repairs:

| Does the wheelchair have a warranty? | ❏ YES | ❏ NO |

| My dog has a different set of special needs than those listed above: | ❏ YES | ❏ NO |

If YES, please explain:

🐾 Dogs that wear special equipment for mobility are no different from humans in that they also chafe and develop pressure sores. Be conscious of how long your dog wears his or her equipment and check areas where skin and equipment come into contact frequently.

🐾 Just because a dog can still physically **DO** something does not necessarily mean they **SHOULD**, particularly when it comes to jumping on and off furniture. If you have an older dog or a dog with physical challenges, consider getting him a small set of stairs or a dog ramp for furniture or getting in and out of the car. This kind of equipment can be purchased at almost any pet supply store. The repeated impact of landing on front paws at steep angles may inevitably have a detrimental effect on shoulder joints, as well as other areas.

Notes:

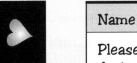

CERTIFICATIONS

Name of dog being rehomed:

Please list any certifications, titles, and/or special designations your dog holds here:

Certifications:

Titles:

Special Designations:

Name of dog being rehomed:

Please list any certifications, titles, and/or special designations your dog holds here:

Certifications:

Titles:

Special Designations:

Notes:

73

Animal Sanctuaries that allow your dog to live at their facility for the remainder of their life; please contact each organization for specific information.

Best Friends Animal Society KANUB, UT
(435) 644-2001
bestfriends.org

Home for Life STILLWATER, MN
(800) 252-5918
homeforlife.org

House with a Heart Senior Pet Sanctuary GAITHERSBURG, MD
(240) 631-1743
housewithaheart.com

Old Friends Senior Dog Sanctuary MT JULIET, TN
(615) 754-5617
ofsds.org

Others:

PLEASE NOTE: The author of this book does not have personal or professional experience with these organizations and cannot guarantee the quality of care that they provide or their ability to accommodate your dog(s). Therefore, you are encouraged to conduct independent research of these organizations to determine whether any of them fit your wishes; the author also cannot guarantee that they are still in operation.

Rehoming organizations that allow your dog to live at their facility OR will adopt them out to an individual home; please contact each organization for specific information:

Hearts United for Animals AUBURN, NE
(402) 274-3679
hua.org

Oasis Animal Sanctuary FRANKLINVILLE, NJ
(856) 262-1222
oasisanimalsanctuary.org

Old Dog Haven LAKE STEVENS, WA
(360) 353-0311
olddoghaven.org

Safe Place for Pets COLORADO SPRINGS, CO
(719) 359-0201
safeplacepets.org

The Milo Foundation WILLITS, CA
(707) 459-4900
milofoundation.org

Others:

Animal Rescues that only work to adopt your pet out to the proper home; please contact each organization for specific information.

Milagro Pet Refuge, Inc. PHOENIX, AZ
(888) 827-4103
milagropets.org

Muttville Senior Dog Rescue SAN FRANCISCO, CA
(415) 272-4172
muttville.org

Paws Guardian Angels Program CHICAGO, IL
(773) 843-2508
pawschicago.org

Peace of Mind Dog Rescue PACIFIC GROVE, CA
(831) 718-9122
peaceofminddogrescue.org

The Sanctuary for Senior Dogs CLEVELAND, OH
(216) 485-9233
sanctuaryforseniordogs.org

Others:

PLEASE NOTE: The author of this book does not have personal or professional experience with these organizations and cannot guarantee the quality of care that they provide or their ability to accommodate your dog(s). Therefore, you are encouraged to conduct independent research of these organizations to determine whether any of them fit your wishes; the author also cannot guarantee that they are still in operation.

ANIMAL SERVICES

Good Karma Pet Services, LLC
Facebook.com/goodkarmapetsitting

Help Finding Lost Dogs in Illinois
Lostdogsillinois.org
Facebook.com/lostdogsillinois

Microchip Registration Company
petlink.net

Microchip Scanner Manufacturer
Datamars.com

Pet Poison Helpline ($59 per incident with follow-up call)
800-213-6680

OTHER SERVICES

Christine Ciana Calabrese, Illinois Licensed Realtor
NextHome Select Realty ▪ HomebuyingISpossible.com
n.facebook.com/ChristineCianaCalabreseRealtor

Guy Youman, Estate Planning, Real Estate and Tax Attorney
The Law offices of Rupp & Youman ▪ **ruppyouman.com**

Sharon Sprague, Writer and Designer
OK Silly Ink ▪ **oksilly.com**

Stacey Edge, Creative Design Firm
MOMENTUM Creative Integration ▪ **momentum-ci.com**

Others:

Christine Ciana Calabrese is a longtime animal lover, advocate and rescuer. She is a previous doggy daycare owner and founder of the former website, PetServicesReview.com. She currently owns and operates the business, **Good Karma Pet Sitting.** Christine is the proud pet parent of Karma, a Cairn Terrier, Tapioca, a Chihuahua-mix, and Pippy, a little demon disguised as a Chihuahua.

Order for a friend!

HOW TO PURCHASE ADDITIONAL COPIES

If you have found this book helpful and would like to purchase additional copies for the dog lovers in your life, please visit **Amazon.com.**

For wholesale inquiries, please e-mail Whataboutthedogbook@gmail.com.

 Whataboutthedogbook

 Facebook.com/Whataboutthedogbook

 Whtabtthedogbk

 #Becauseourdogisfamily

Notes:

11883939R00051

Made in the USA
Monee, IL
18 September 2019